Daily Warm-Ups

MYTHOLOGY

Level II

1 2 3 4 5 6 7 8 9 10
ISBN 0-8251-4631-3

Walch Publishing
P. O. Box 658 • Portland, Maine 04104-0658
www.walch.com

Printed in the United States of America

The *Daily Warm-Ups* series is a wonderful way to turn extra classroom minutes into valuable learning time. The 180 quick activities—one for each day of the school year—review Greek, Roman, and Norse mythology. These daily activities may be used at the very beginning of class to get students into learning mode, near the end of class to make good educational use of that transitional time, in the middle of class to shift gears between lessons—or whenever else you have minutes that now go unused. In addition to providing students with fascinating information, they are a natural path to other classroom activities involving critical thinking.

Daily Warm-Ups are easy-to-use reproducibles—simply photocopy the day's activity and distribute it. Or make a transparency of the activity and project it on the board. You may want to use the activities for extra credit points or as a check on a knowledge of mythology that is built and acquired over time.

However you choose to use them, *Daily Warm-Ups* are a convenient and useful supplement to your regular lesson plans. Make every minute of your class time count!

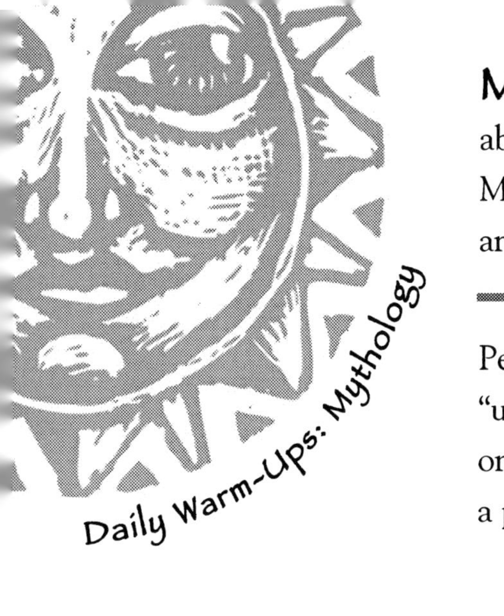

Myths are stories that reveal important questions about birth and death, love and hate, hardship and justice. Mythology is the study of these stories and the gods, heroes, and humans that populate them.

People often use the word *myth* to suggest that an idea is "unreal." Does it matter if a story literally took place? Reveal one of your own ideas about the human condition by writing a paragraph about a fictional person.

An enduring question for all cultures is "Did the universe have a beginning?" Greek mythology suggests that everything sprang from Chaos, an *abyss* or *the unknown*. The earth, Gaia, rose up from Chaos, according to the Greek poet Hesiod.

What is the difference between rising up from nothing and rising up from the unknown? Explain.

Gaia, the earth, was born because of Eros, or *attraction*. Before Gaia, the atoms of all that existed were in a confused flux.

Why might attraction, or love, be necessary for things like the sky and Earth to form? Write your ideas below.

The first gods and goddesses, such as Gaia and Uranus, were not as personable as later gods. They were more primitive and had less defined personalities. Nyx, or Night, is another such goddess. She is the mother of old age, sleep, and death.

What do these three things have in common with the night? What do you think nyctophobes fear? Write your answers below.

According to the Roman poet Ovid, the history of humans is separated into four ages. The earliest period was the Golden Age. Ovid lived in a period he called the Iron Age.

Match the name of an age with the description from Ovid. Write the letter of the correct answer in the space provided.

___ 1. The Iron Age

___ 2. The Bronze Age

___ 3. The Silver Age

___ 4. The Golden Age

a. People live in ease and abundance, in a sort of paradise.

b. People live as immature beings, and seasons appear.

c. Hardship appears, and people are fashioned from ash wood.

d. Toil and fighting are common.

Now write a paragraph describing the age you live in. What do you call your age? Why?

At the beginning of the Iron Age, humans were unable to use fire. Prometheus, whose name means *forethought*, stole fire from Zeus and brought it to Earth in a stalk of fennel. Prometheus' brother was Epimetheus, whose name means *hindsight*.

Which would you rather have, forethought or hindsight? What are the benefits of each attribute? Write your thoughts below.

Furious over the theft of fire, Zeus sent to Earth the first woman, Pandora. She arrived with a jar of "gifts." Zeus had told her not to open the jar, but Pandora couldn't resist doing so. When she opened the jar, afflictions escaped and spread throughout the world. Vice, anger, insanity, and lust are now a curse to humankind. But Zeus told Pandora to plug the jar before hope could escape.

What can hope do for people? Why is it necessary? What is a *Pandora's box*? Write your thoughts below.

Myths were created before the era of literacy. Long before they were first written down, they survived by being told or recited.

What are the advantages and disadvantages of passing down stories orally? Make a list of advantages and disadvantages below, and explain your reasoning.

Classics is the study of the ancient literature of Greece and Rome.

What do people mean when they use the word *classical?* Can you circle the three great dramatists of classical Athens below?

Apollodorus	Gaia
Zeus	Virgil
Aeschylus	Sophocles
Hesiod	Homer
Euripides	Ovid

Before becoming the leader of the Olympian gods, Zeus warred with his father, Cronus. Out of jealousy, Cronus actually swallowed his own children. Zeus wanted to free himself and his siblings. He wanted to make his own decisions and act for himself.

Do you identify with Zeus? Why? Write a paragraph explaining your thoughts.

Zeus, Poseidon, and Hades controlled their own realms. Each god was given a tool by the Cyclopes. Zeus was given a thunderbolt. Poseidon received a trident. Hades had a cap of invisibility.

What three realms did these gods control? Circle the letter of the correct answer.

a. rivers, streams, lakes

b. mountains, islands, valleys

c. fields, forests, deserts

d. the sky, the sea, the underworld

Invent another appropriate tool each for Zeus, Poseidon, and Hades.

Poseidon was the god of the sea. Describe the sea. How does it move? What are its qualities?

Based on your description, circle the letter of the things below that Poseidon might logically control.

a. plants and flowers

b. snakes and lizards

c. horses and earthquakes

d. fire and heat

Metis was the first wife of Zeus. Zeus learned that if Metis bore him a son, that child would overthrow Zeus. To avoid this, Zeus swallowed Metis while she was pregnant. Metis, a goddess and immortal, gave birth to a daughter inside Zeus. After this happened, Zeus experienced an agonizing headache. To help him, Hephaestus opened Zeus' head with an ax. Out sprang Athena, fully clothed in armor.

How is this birth similar to a conventional birth? How is it different? Why might gods sometimes be born as fully formed adults? Write your ideas below.

Hephaestus was the misshapen son of Hera. An ugly infant, he was cast out of Olympus by his mother and landed on the island of Lemnos. There he learned to forge incredible inventions. Later, he was allowed back into Olympus because his inventions were so useful and beautiful.

Describe someone you know who was shunned at first but later welcomed for his or her expertise. Has this happened to you? How would you feel if you were Hephaestus?

Ares, the god of war, was disliked by the other gods. His sacred bird was the vulture.

Hades, the god of the underworld, didn't hate Ares. Why? What do you think the relationship might have been between these two gods? Write your ideas below.

Ares was thought to be a coward and was not liked by the other gods. Diomedes, the mortal King of Aetolia, stabbed Ares in the battle at Troy, and the god of war fled in terror to his father.

Why would Ares be disliked? Is fighting a cowardly or a brave thing to do? Explain your ideas.

King Midas heard Pan and Apollo competing in a music contest. Pan played a reed pipe and Apollo played a silver lyre. Pan's playing was crude and foolish, but Midas judged it to be better. Angry, Apollo gave Midas the ears of an ass.

Why did Apollo choose this punishment? What else could Apollo have done? Write your ideas below.

Helios, the sun god, drove his chariot through the sky, bringing day to the world. One day his mortal son, Phaëthon, asked to be granted one wish. Helios agreed, but he immediately regretted doing so. Phaëthon asked to drive the sun chariot for one day. Helios tried to change his son's mind, but it was no use.

Daily Warm-Ups: Mythology

Based on your knowledge of mythology, do you think this story ends happily? Why or why not? What might have happened to Phaëthon? Write your thoughts below.

As the sun god, Helios had an extraordinary sense of sight. He saw everything.

Why was this sense appropriate for Helios? Why were the other senses of less importance for him? Explain your thoughts in a paragraph.

Helios, the sun, had two sisters. Their names were Eos and Selene.

Given their relationship to Helios, which of the descriptions below probably fit them? Circle the letter of your choice.

a. goddesses of meadows and forests

b. goddesses of streams and lakes

c. goddesses of dawn and moonlight

d. goddesses of rains and harvest

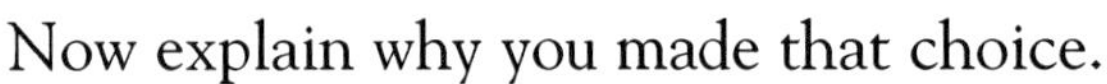

Now explain why you made that choice.

There are a few versions of the story of Endymion, a very beautiful young man. In one version, Zeus asked Endymion if he wanted to determine his own destiny. Endymion said he wanted to preserve his beauty. Zeus maintained Endymion's beauty by causing him to sleep for the rest of time.

Is that too high a price to pay for good looks? What does this story say about beauty? Write your thoughts below.

In mythology, mortals are closely connected to nature. Their stories involve natural things, such as trees, flowers, clouds, and the sea. The gods and goddesses are often a part of nature, representing the sun or the moon, for example.

In a paragraph, explain whether or not you feel close to nature. What connects you to or separates you from it?

One of the Olympian gods was honored through drinking wine, dancing, and revelry.

Which god is this? Circle the letter of your answer.

a. Athena

b. Zeus

c. Dionysus

d. Demeter

e. Poseidon

Now describe an encounter with this god. Would you be frightened or disgusted by this god? Explain.

Another wild god was Pan, from whose name comes the word *panic*. He spent much of his time in the mountains, playing his pipes and chasing nymphs. In battle or in the forest, he would let out a terrifying shout.

What does it mean to panic? Write a paragraph about it.

Dionysus once granted a wish to Midas, King of Phrygia, for being a generous host. Midas wanted everything he touched to turn to gold. Unfortunately for Midas, his wish came true. He could not even eat, because the food turned to metal when it touched his lips.

What do you think this story says about the desire for wealth? What does it say about wishes? Write your thoughts below.

In the *Iliad*, Hera reminds Zeus that fate is the one thing the all-powerful god cannot change.

What does the word *fate* mean? Have you ever felt that something was destined to happen? Can you overcome fate? Explain your ideas.

Dictys was fishing in the sea when he spotted a wooden chest. Inside was baby Perseus. Dictys took the baby into his own home and helped to raise him.

Does this story remind you of any others? If so, summarize them here. If not, write a short story about someone who does find a baby, and tell what the person does to handle the situation.

Perseus offered to bring Polydectes anything he desired in celebration of his wedding. Polydectes asked for the head of Medusa. Medusa was one of the Gorgons, with snakes sprouting from her head in place of hair. She had large wings, and scales covered her body. Anyone who looked at her was immediately turned to stone.

Draw a picture of what you imagine Medusa looked like.

To successfully kill Medusa, Perseus needed certain gifts from the nymphs of the North. Only the Gray Women knew where these nymphs lived. The Gray Women were three sisters, strange creatures with only one eye among them. When one sister had the eye in her forehead, the other two were blind. They took turns using the eye. To force the Gray Women to tell the secret of where the nymphs lived, Perseus stole the eye and threatened to keep it. The sisters quickly told their secret.

Hermes gave Perseus this plan. Do you have any other ideas Perseus could have tried to get the information? Team up with a classmate and brainstorm some ideas.

Perseus slayed Medusa by using a shield in a unique way. Instead of shielding himself against a sword or spear, he used the shiny metal as a mirror to spy on her. (Looking at her directly would have killed him instantly.) Once he saw that she was asleep, he cut off her head.

This was an ingenious plan. Describe a time when you fixed a problem in a clever way.

As Perseus was going home after killing Medusa, he stopped to rest with the Hesperides. Their father was Atlas, a Titan. Atlas was afraid that Perseus would steal their Golden Apples. Perseus still had the head of Medusa in his bag. He showed Medusa's head to Atlas.

Given what you know about Medusa, what happened to Atlas? Since he was a Titan, what kind of landform did he become? Where is Atlas located today? Write your answers below.

Many Greek gods were adopted by the Romans and renamed.

Sort the following names of the gods and goddesses into two groups: one for Greek, the other for Roman.

Zeus	Mars
Neptune	Aphrodite
Athena	Jupiter
Ares	Poseidon
Venus	Minerva

When Perseus came upon Andromeda chained to a rock and waiting to be eaten by a sea monster, she begged him to save her. She offered to be his slave.

Andromeda was desperate, and Perseus could have asked her to do anything in return for his helping her. Perseus decided that he would not only save her but that she would be his wife, not his slave. What does this say about the hero Perseus? Write your ideas below.

Perseus killed his grandfather, Acrisius, by mistake. He threw a discus at a funeral game and it hit his grandfather. It had been prophesied that Perseus would kill Acrisius. Though the two had fought in the past, at the time of Acrisius' death, they had made amends.

What is a *prophecy*? Do you believe a prophecy can be real? Explain.

Perseus was devastated by his grandfather's death. He was embarrassed by his tragic throw. Instead of inheriting his grandfather's kingdom, he felt he had to leave it.

Do you understand why Perseus could not accept the kingdom? Explain how you would have felt if you were Perseus. What would you have done?

The goddess Demeter lost her daughter to Hades, the king of the underworld. Hades had abducted Persephone and taken her to his realm. While looking for her, Demeter destroyed crops everywhere she went. Humanity was starving. Zeus arranged for Persephone to go back and forth between the underworld and Olympus. The earth was made fertile again. But every year when Persephone returned to the underworld, trees dropped their fruit and flowers withered.

What fact of nature does this story illustrate? What do modern people attribute this change to? Write your answers below.

Sisyphus is one of the craftier men in mythology. He suspected that cattle from his herd were being stolen by Autolycus and placed nearby in his herd. Sisyphus tricked Autolycus by signing the bottom of the hooves of his cattle. They read, "Stolen by Autolycus."

Think of another way Sisyphus could have tricked Autolycus. Keep in mind that Autolycus could change any spot or mark on a cattle's hide, so a tattoo would not work. Write your idea below.

Because of his irreverence toward Zeus and Hades, Sisyphus was not liked. He once locked Thanatos, the god of Death, in chains. He cheated his way out of the underworld by tricking Persephone. Finally, as punishment for these acts, he was condemned to push a boulder up a hill in the underworld for eternity. Before he could reach the top of the hill, the boulder always rolled back down.

How would you feel if you were Sisyphus? How would you try to get out of this punishment? Explain.

Tantalus also suffered in the underworld. He was a rich king who stole the gods' ambrosia and nectar just to impress his mortal friends. He served his own son, Pelops, as a dish at a banquet because he was afraid of running out of food. As punishment, Tantalus was hung from a tree in the underworld. Whenever he reached for fruit hanging above him, a wind would lift it away. Whenever he bent to drink some water pooled below him, it would recede.

Can you see where the word *tantalizing* comes from? Define *tantalizing* and use it in a sentence. Then explain why this punishment is perfect for Tantalus.

There are many talented musicians in mythology, but Orpheus was considered the best lyrist. When he played, everything stopped for the performance: Rivers ceased flowing, and trees bent their boughs just to listen.

Have you ever been captivated by a piece of music? Write a paragraph about a time when you were fascinated by the sound of an instrument.

Orpheus traveled to the underworld to find his wife, Eurydice. Because of his beautiful playing, the guard, the three-headed dog Cerberus, allowed him to pass. Orpheus enchanted Hades and Persephone. They let him lead his wife to the surface of the earth by the sound of his lyre. He was forbidden to look back at her, however, until they both reached the light. Orpheus made it to the light first, but he looked back, and his wife faded away.

Is there something that you find impossible to resist doing? Was it fair that Orpheus lost his wife? Explain.

Many Greek gods were adopted by the Romans and renamed.

Sort the following names of the gods and goddesses into two groups: one for Greek, the other for Roman.

Juno	Artemis
Diana	Hera
Hermes	Mercury
Vulcan	Hephaestus

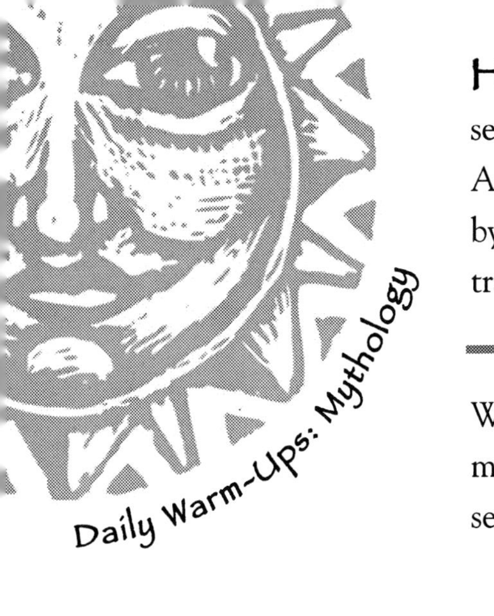

Humans often suffer in mythology when they see things the gods don't want them to see. Actaeon saw Artemis bathing. She turned him into a stag, and he was killed by his own dogs. Semele asked to see Zeus' true form. He transformed into a lightning bolt, and she was burned to death.

Write a paragraph explaining what you think these stories mean. Are there things in nature that humans should never see? Do humans have a right to see everything?

If Laius had a child with Jocasta, said the oracle at Delphi, then the child would kill Laius and bring utter ruin to the city of Thebes. Jocasta gave birth to a boy, Oedipus, and Laius had the infant abandoned on Mount Cithaeron.

What would you have done if you were Laius? The oracle said the whole city would be ruined by Oedipus. Does that make a difference to your response? Write your answer below.

When Oedipus and Laius met at a narrow crossroads, with one path headed for Daulis and the other for Delphi, they both refused to move out of the way. Laius' servant told Oedipus to yield to his social better. Oedipus said he would step aside only for his father or a god. Someone hit Oedipus, there was a fight, and Laius was killed.

Who was at fault? Who should have moved aside? Why? Explain your thoughts below.

Thebes was being terrorized by the Sphinx. She ate everyone who was unable to answer her riddle. She had the head of a woman, the body of a lion, the tail of a snake, and the wings of an eagle.

Draw a picture of the Sphinx.

The Sphinx asked, "What creature walks on four legs in the morning, two in the daytime, and three in the evening?"

Oedipus answered correctly. What did he say? Can you think of another correct answer? Write your answers below.

The answer to the Sphinx's riddle is "man." Mythology tries to help us understand humankind. In a sense, *we* are the riddle.

What don't you understand about yourself? Write a short myth that explains something confusing about human nature.

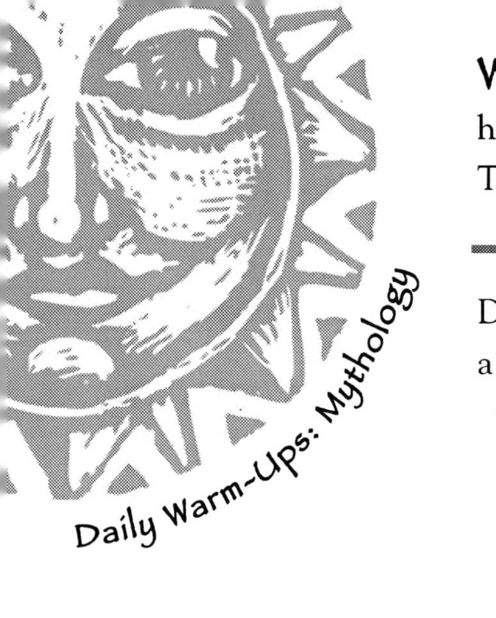

When Oedipus solved the riddle, the Sphinx killed herself. Oedipus won the hand of Jocasta and the throne of Thebes. The city was free from the murderous monster.

Do his actions and their results make Oedipus a hero? What is a hero? List as many heroes as you can from films or novels.

Oedipus might have been the cleverest man in Thebes. He was the only one who could solve the Sphinx's riddle and free the city. But there were two things about himself that he did not know: He had killed his father, and he had married his mother.

It is ironic that Oedipus, who was so clever, didn't know these things. What does *ironic* mean? Write a paragraph about something else that is ironic.

Oedipus was overwhelmed when he learned about his family and realized what he had done. Taking a brooch from Jocasta, he blinded himself.

Why did Oedipus put his eyes out? What do you think is the meaning of this act? Write your ideas below.

Zeus asked Athena to help him trick Hera. He wanted Hera to breast-feed his newborn son, Heracles (Hercules). Athena brought the infant to Hera and claimed that he had been abandoned. Heracles suckled with a terrible force. When Hera tore him from her breast, the spilled milk created the Milky Way.

Write your own myth that explains how the Milky Way was created. You may use people from your life as the characters in the story, if you wish.

Heracles was famous for his strength and endurance. He was also famous for having learned skills from many teachers.

Match each teacher with the subjects he taught Heracles. Write the correct letter in the space provided.

___ 1. Amphitryon	a. boxing
___ 2. Autolycus	b. chariot driving
___ 3. Castor	c. literature
___ 4. Eumolpus	d. archery
___ 5. Eurytus	e. fencing
___ 6. Linus	f. singing and music

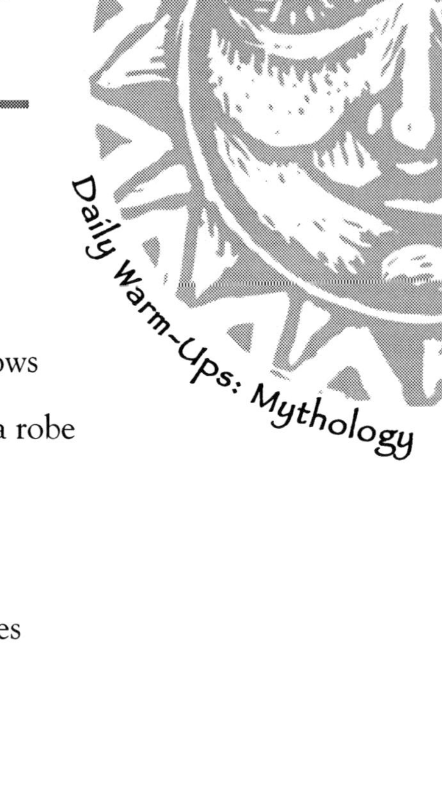

Heracles' weapons and armor were given to him by many of the Olympians.

Match each gift given to Heracles with its giver. Write the correct letter in the space provided.

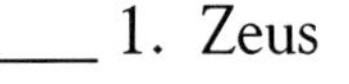

___ 1. Zeus	a. a bow and arrows
___ 2. Athena	b. a helmet and a robe
___ 3. Apollo	c. a shield
___ 4. Hermes	d. a sword
___ 5. Hephaestus	e. a team of horses
___ 6. Poseidon	f. a breastplate

Heracles was made insane by Hera, and he committed many crimes in a state of madness. Pythia, the oracle at Delphi, told him to see King Eurystheus, who would give him ten labors to do to atone for his crimes. His first labor was to kill the terrible Nemean lion. Although his weapons were given to him by the gods, they were unable to penetrate the lion's skin. Instead of using a weapon to kill the Nemean lion, Heracles strangled it.

Lions often kill their prey by strangulation. What do you think this says about Heracles? Write your thoughts below.

When Heracles returned to King Eurystheus after killing the Nemean lion, the king was terrified of the hero's lion-skin cloak.

Why would the king be afraid? What was intimidating about Heracles' accomplishment? Explain your ideas.

King Eurystheus ordered a huge bronze jar to be put in the ground. The king wanted a place to hide from Heracles when the hero returned from his labors.

Describe in a paragraph how you think King Eurystheus felt when the powerful Heracles came to visit him after completing a dangerous, nearly impossible task. What does it mean for a king to hide in this manner?

The second labor of Heracles was the killing of the Lernaean Hydra. This hideous monster had a dog's body and many snakelike heads. Its breath was poisonous. Whenever Heracles cut off one of the Hydra's heads, it grew back in twos.

Write a paragraph about a time you tried to fix or change something but only made the problem worse with each attempt.

King Eurystheus did not accept Heracles' killing of the Lernaean Hydra as one of the ten labors because Heracles had the help of Iolaus. Pythia told Heracles that he must accomplish any ten tasks that King Eurystheus named.

Write two paragraphs, one explaining why the second labor should have counted and the other telling why it should not have counted.

Heracles dipped his arrows in the poisonous blood of the Lernaean Hydra. One of the arrows accidentally hit Cheiron, Heracles' friend who had taught him manners and decorum. Another arrow slipped from the hand of Pholus, hit his foot, and killed him.

Are some weapons too dangerous to keep? Or was the problem with Heracles? Explain your opinion.

Heracles' third labor was to capture the Ceryneian stag and bring it alive to King Eurystheus. This deer was sacred to Artemis, and it had golden antlers and brass hoofs.

There are many examples in literature of people pursuing something beautiful and fleeting. Write a poem or a paragraph about pursuing something like the Ceryneian stag.

Heracles' fifth labor was the cleaning of the stables of King Augeas. These stables had not been cleaned in thirty years, and they housed three thousand cattle.

Describe the dirtiest job that you have ever done. Why did you have to do this job? How did the job get so dirty? How can you avoid having to do it again?

Heracles cleaned the Augean stables by diverting the rivers Alpheus and Peneus. These waterways rushed through the stalls and washed away the debris. King Augeas agreed to pay Heracles ten percent of his cattle once the stalls were clean. After completing this labor, Augeas claimed that Heracles owed Eurystheus the task as a penance and that Augeas should not have to pay him. Eurystheus claimed that the task did not count as one of Heracles' ten labors because he had done it to gain Augeas' cattle.

Should the fifth labor count for Heracles as one of the ten that he owed Eurystheus? Do you think Augeas and Eurystheus were too strict in their rules? Explain.

Cleaning the Augean stables by hand would have taken weeks. Heracles was able to clean them in a day because he had an idea to use the rivers Alpheus and Peneus and the power to do it.

Describe, in a paragraph, a big problem that you could solve with a good idea. Are there any negative consequences to this idea? Explain.

Heracles' sixth labor was to rid Lake Stymphalus of its enormous flock of man-eating birds. He did so by frightening them with a pair of bronze castanets.

Birds are often graceful, but the Stymphalian birds had long legs, claws, wings of bronze, and poisonous excrement. Write a paragraph about something that does not look or behave as you would expect.

Heracles's eighth labor was to capture the man-eating horses of King Diomedes. Diomedes had trained his horses to eat the flesh of his guests. When Heracles caught the horses, Diomedes pursued him. Eventually, Diomedes was fed to his horses. He was destroyed by his own invention.

Characters in mythology often suffer when they try to alter natural laws. We have already seen what happened to Endymion when he tried to change the law of aging. List some other laws of nature that people would like to change. Then write a myth about what happens when one of those laws is changed.

Heracles' eleventh labor was to steal the Golden Apples from the Garden of the Hesperides in the western part of the Mediterranean.

In mythology and literature, fruit is often highly desirable. What are the qualities of fruit that make characters want it? What stories or ideas do you associate with fruit? Explain.

When Heracles arrived at the Garden of the Hesperides, he spoke to Nereus, who convinced him to trick Atlas into picking the Golden Apples. Atlas, a Titan, was busy holding up the sky and the earth that floated in it.

What does it mean when someone “carries the weight of the world”? How might such a burden be lessened? Describe what you would do to help someone who feels such a burden.

When Atlas returned from the garden with the apples, Heracles was holding up the sky. Atlas was not excited about resuming his burden. Heracles knew that Atlas wanted to trade places. He asked Atlas to hold the sky again for just a minute while he put a cushion on top of his head to ease the load. Once Atlas took the weight back, he was stuck with it.

How would you describe Atlas? Has anything like this happened to you? If so, how did you feel about it? If not, how do you think you would feel? Write your thoughts below.

Heracles' last labor was dragging the guard dog of Hades, Cerberus, up to the surface of the earth. Cerberus had three heads, a powerful body, and the tail of a dragon.

Draw a picture of Cerberus.

After marrying Deianira, Heracles and his wife were crossing the Evenus River. A centaur named Nessus offered to ferry Deianira across the river. After the three set off together, Nessus tried to abduct Deianira. Heracles shot him with a poisoned arrow. As the centaur was dying, he pretended to be sorry and gave Deianira his bloody shirt as a charm: If Heracles ever loved another woman, Deianira could win him back by having him wear the shirt. However, when Heracles put the shirt on, the poison in the centaur's blood burned his skin. Heracles became his own last victim.

Deianira is sometimes called "naive." What does this word mean to you? Do you think it is a good description of Deianira? List three adjectives to describe each character in this myth: Nessus, Deianira, Heracles.

Match each character from the stories of Heracles with his or her description. Write the letter of the correct answer in the space provided.

___ 1. Alcmene	a. the father of Heracles
___ 2. Alcestis	b. was beaten by Heracles in a fight
___ 3. Antaeus	c. the King of Thebes
___ 4. Creon	d. was rescued from the underworld
___ 5. Zeus	e. the mother of Heracles
___ 6. Megara	f. the first wife of Heracles

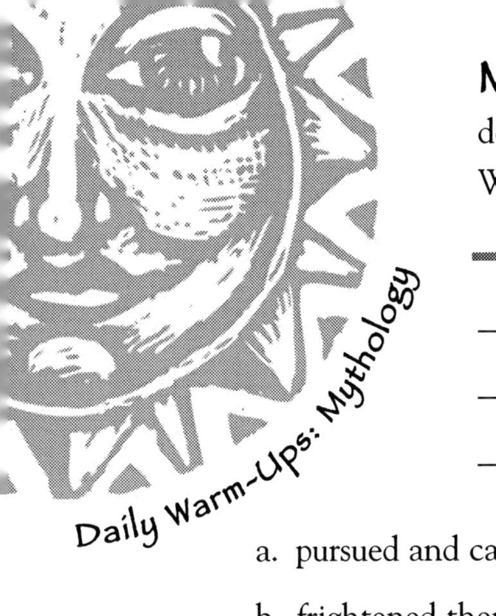

Match the name of each labor of Heracles with the description of what the hero did while completing the labor. Write the letter of the correct answer in the space provided.

___ 1. Nemean lion

___ 2. Lernaean Hydra

___ 3. Ceryneian stag

___ 4. Stymphalian birds

___ 5. Augean stables

___ 6. Horses of Diomedes

a. pursued and caught for its golden antlers and brass hoofs

b. frightened them off with a pair of castanets

c. made them eat their own master

d. cleaned it in a day with two rivers, Alpheus and Peneus

e. cut off its many heads

f. made a cloak of its hide

Think about all the stories you know about Heracles.

Which is your favorite story from the myth of Heracles? Describe what happens in the story and explain why you like it.

The story of Jason begins with his journey to the kingdom of Iolcus. Jason was determined to take back the throne from his uncle, Pelias.

Families often disagree about legacies or inheritances even when there is nothing at stake financially. Write a paragraph about one such agreement or disagreement you have experienced or have read about.

Athamas was a Greek king whose people demanded that he sacrifice his son, Phrixus, to ensure their corn would grow. As Athamas was preparing to sacrifice Phrixus with a knife, a golden ram sent by Hermes appeared and flew off with Phrixus and his sister, Helle. This ram's hide became the Golden Fleece.

Why might a story of a stopped sacrifice be important to people in understanding their relationship with their gods? Explain.

Jason was the rightful heir to a throne that had been taken by his uncle, Pelias. To get rid of Jason, Pelias promised to give up the kingdom if Jason brought back the Golden Fleece from Colchis.

What does the name *Golden Fleece* suggest to you? Imagine what it might look like and describe it as completely as you can.

Jason's ship, the *Argo*, was traditionally considered the first ship ever constructed. It is said that Athena taught the crew how to sail.

How do you think the *Argo* was invented? If you had to create the first ship, how would you go about planning and testing it? Explain your ideas.

The women of Lemnos failed to honor Aphrodite. The goddess plagued them with a foul odor, and their husbands replaced the women with captives from Thrace.

This crude story illustrates that humans are attracted to each other because of certain characteristics. Write a paragraph explaining your ideas about attraction. What attracts you to someone? What makes you feel uncomfortable about a person? What do people do to make themselves more attractive?

When Jason and the Argonauts arrived at Lemnos, they were welcomed by the husbandless Lemnian wives. Many members of the crew lingered on the island and seemed ready to settle down with the women. Heracles, who was along for the adventure, sent a message from the boat, asking if pleasure and wives were what the Argonauts truly wanted.

We all have to forgo pleasure in order to accomplish certain things. Describe a time when you gave something up to accomplish something else.

After leaving the peninsula of Cyzicus, the Argonauts ran into fog and headwinds. They were forced to land for the night. Soon a band of men surprised them and a bloody fight ensued. By morning, many dead lay on the beach, and the Argonauts realized they had been fighting their friends the Doliones.

How could the Argonauts make this mistake? How would you feel if you had spent all night fighting your friends only to realize it in the morning? Explain.

Stopping in Salmydessus, the Argonauts found Phineus, a soothsayer who was being punished by Zeus for telling the future. Whenever Phineus tried to eat, the Harpies would descend and steal his food or pollute it. Phineus had grown meek and withered.

If you could tell the future, what would you do with the knowledge? Would you be able to keep it to yourself? Why would the gods not want a mortal to predict events? Write your thoughts below.

At the end of the Bosporus Strait, the Argonauts reached the Clashing Rocks. Phineus told them to release a dove and see if it could fly between the floating boulders. When the bird safely made it, the crew rowed through and lost only an ornament from the *Argo's* stern. Athena had taught the Argonauts how to sail. She is also said to have held the Clashing Rocks open to let the *Argo* pass.

Write a paragraph about a skill that someone has taught you. Did it take you a long time to learn it? Do you think about your teacher's advice when you practice the skill?

A horrible serpent guarded the Golden Fleece. Jason seized the Golden Fleece after Medea, a sorceress, charmed the serpent to sleep with a magical song.

Certain images—things that appeal to our senses—can transport us. What happens when you are charmed by something? Describe the feeling.

On the way to the island of Drepane, the Argonauts steered through a narrow passage between the cliffs of Scylla and the whirlpool of Charybdis. If they steered too much in one direction, they would crash into the cliffs. If they steered too much in the other direction, they would be sucked into the whirlpool.

The voyagers had a problem on either side of them. Describe a time you had to navigate a situation perfectly. How did you feel during this ordeal? How did you feel when it was over?

When the Argonauts sailed near the island of Anthemoessa, the Sirens called to them. It was the Sirens' strategy to lure sailors with their singing, only to let them die of hunger. Orpheus protected his fellow voyagers by playing his lyre over the sound of the Sirens, drowning it out.

Orpheus created a shield around the Argonauts. List the shields that you use and what they protect you from. (Sunblock is one example.)

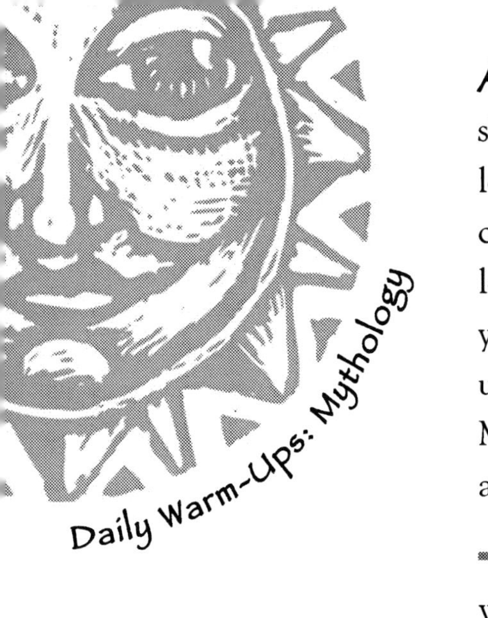

After the Argonauts returned to Iolcus, Medea slipped into the city and convinced the daughters of Pelias to let her restore his youth with a trick. Medea had an old ram cut into pieces. She made a stew and said a spell, and a lamb leaped from the pot. This same process would make Pelias young again, said Medea, if his daughters would only cut him up. Of course, after the daughters of Pelias had cut him up, Medea refused to perform the spell. Thus, Jason was finally able to take over the kingdom.

Why do people want to remain young or recapture their youth? Does anyone ever succeed in doing this? List some advantages of old age. Compare your list with those of classmates.

Sort the following words into two groups: one related to the adventures of Heracles and the other related to the adventures of the Argonauts.

Golden Apples	Clashing Rocks
The Harpies	Lernaean Hydra
Lemnian wives	Cerberus
Scylla and Charybdis	Nemean lion
Stymphalian birds	Dolione tribe

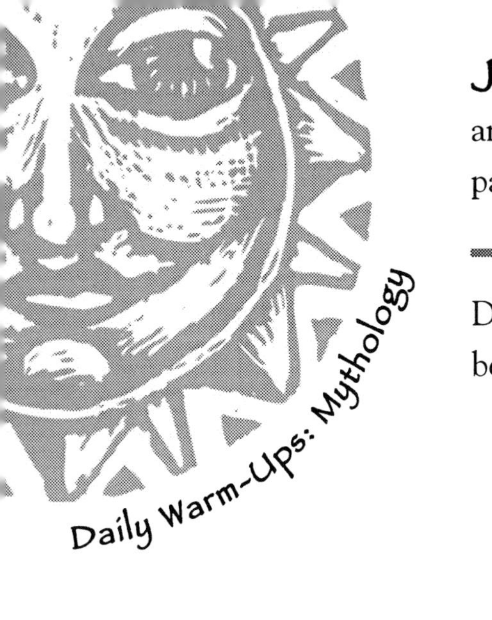

Journeys like the quest for the Golden Fleece are common in mythology. Indeed, journeys play an important part in the literature and cultures of the world.

Describe a challenge that you would like to undertake. It could be a physical, an intellectual, or an emotional challenge.

King Aegeus of Athens was unable to have a child until he met and loved Aethra. Aegeus buried his sword and sandals under a boulder. He told Aethra that if she had a boy she should send him to Athens when he was strong enough to push aside the boulder and find Aegeus' belongings. Aegeus would recognize his son by the sword and sandals.

The idea of a son wearing a father's equipment is stirring. What do you think it signifies? What does it mean to "come of age"? Write your thoughts below.

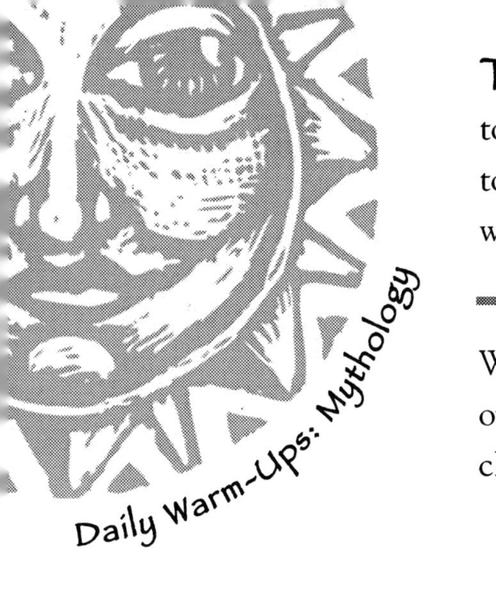

Theseus did not choose the safe way to get to Athens, sailing across the Saronic Gulf. The youthful hero took a dangerous land route instead, filled with bandits. He wanted to prove himself as great a hero as his cousin Heracles.

What do you think of Theseus' choice of route? Make a list of the pros and cons of his decision. Share your list with a classmate.

Theseus confronted Periphetes in the town of Epidaurus. Periphetes had a custom of beating travelers with a club that his father, Hephaestus, made for him. After a struggle, Theseus smashed Periphetes with the club and killed him.

Characters in mythology often suffer the same treatment that they inflict on others. What do you think of Theseus' brand of justice? Does the semi-divine nature of some of Theseus' foes affect your opinion? Explain.

When Theseus arrived in Athens, he was wearing a long robe. The men in Athens wore short tunics and laughed at the hero because he looked like a woman.

What is customary clothing for men and women in your culture? Would people ridicule you for wearing a tunic or a robe? List some places where you would need to wear a style of clothing different from what you are accustomed to.

Not yet knowing who Theseus was, King Aegeus was afraid that the impressive young man would try to take his throne. He knew that Pallas, his own brother, had fifty sons and wanted the kingdom for himself.

Kings in mythology are often afraid of being overthrown. They sometimes kill their own children in succession disputes. Describe this world of mythological kings. How would it feel to worry constantly about maintaining your kingdom? Would holding on to power be worth violence? Explain.

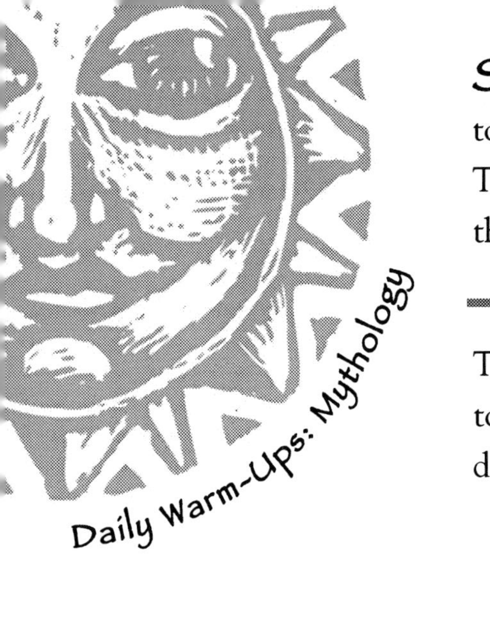

Still unaware of who Theseus was, Aegeus asked him to kill the Marathonian bull, also known as the Cretan bull. The skillful Theseus grabbed the bull by the horns and subdued the beast with a rope. He then led it back to Athens.

This is a familiar scenario in mythology. What does the ability to control a savage beast say about a hero? How would you describe Theseus? Write your description below.

Pasiphae was the wife of King Minos. The Minotaur was the offspring of Pasiphae and a bull. This monster had the body of a man and the head of a bull, with horns and large, dark eyes. Minos couldn't bring himself to destroy the dangerous monster, so he had Daedalus build the Labyrinth. This was a complex maze from which the Minotaur could not escape.

Draw a picture of the Minotaur. Would you consider the Minotaur to be a man, a bull, or something else?

In revenge for the loss of his son while visiting Aegeus, Minos demanded that Athens send young Athenians to be eaten by the Minotaur. To stop the sacrificing of Athenian youths, Theseus had to find the Minotaur in its Labyrinth, kill the monster, and get back out. Ariadne, a daughter of Minos and Pasiphae, gave Theseus a ball of twine to ensure his return from the Labyrinth.

How do you think Theseus used the twine? Can you think of any other way Theseus might have found his way out of the Labyrinth? Explain.

After leaving Crete, Theseus and his companions sailed on to the island of Naxos. Theseus left Ariadne on the island and departed. Because he forgot Ariadne, the gods punished him. Instead of remembering to hoist a white sail of success as he returned to Athens, Theseus sailed with the black one of despair. His father Aegeus assumed that Theseus was dead because of the black sail, and he leaped into the sea to his death.

What do you think of Theseus' punishment? What lesson might people draw from this part of the Theseus story? Write your ideas below.

Hippolytus was a son of Theseus. The young man ignored Aphrodite and refused to get involved in love affairs. As punishment, Aphrodite caused Phaedra, Theseus' second wife, to fall in love with Hippolytus, who rejected her. Then Phaedra falsely accused Hippolytus of rape. In a rage, Theseus asked Poseidon to destroy his son. Poseidon complied, sending a vast sea monster that drove Hippolytus to his death.

Why do you think Phaedra did this terrible thing? Explain how you think Phaedra must have felt when Hippolytus rejected her. How must she have felt after discovering her false accusation led to Hippolytus' death?

Theseus is considered one of the fathers of democracy. He resigned his royal status at Athens and formed a commonwealth in which all citizens were relatively equal.

What are some of the crucial aspects of a democracy? How does a democracy work? Would you rather live under a monarch or an elected politician? Explain.

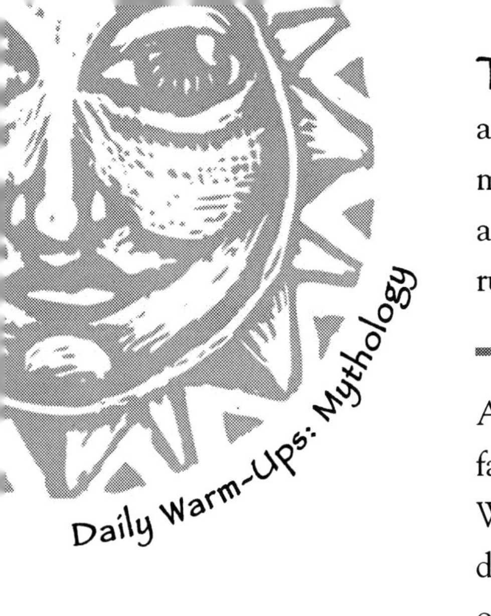

Theseus' ghost marched before the Athenians as they fought the Persians at the Battle of Marathon. His memory rallied the soldiers to fight for their city. There was a saying that captures the Athenians' respect for this early ruler: "Nothing without Theseus."

Athenians felt they owed Theseus for bringing democracy and fairness to their city. Write a paragraph about your country. Who is responsible for your country's political system? If you decided to defend your country, would you invoke the memory of a past leader? If so, who?

The Trojan War might be the most famous event in classical mythology.

You probably have impressions about what happened in the war, where it happened, and who was involved. Write a paragraph about the Trojan War.

Classical mythology is filled with tales of conflict and war.

Would you be willing to fight for your country? Are there good and bad reasons for going to war? Explain your feelings.

Eris, the goddess of discord, played a crucial role in starting the Trojan War.

What does *discord* mean? Have you ever experienced discord? Is it different from *argument*? Explain your thoughts in a paragraph.

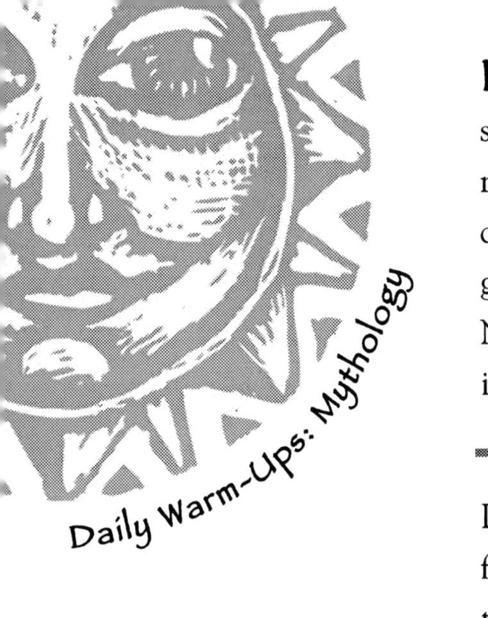

Eris was not a popular goddess because of the fighting she inspired. After this goddess, also known as Discord, was not invited to the marriage of King Peleus and Thetis, she decided to make trouble. She tossed into the banquet hall a golden apple with the words *For the Fairest* engraved on it. Naturally, several goddesses believed themselves to be the intended recipient of the apple.

Draw a picture of what this scene might have looked like. Use facial expressions and physical characteristics you know about the goddesses to differentiate them.

Hera, Athena, and Aphrodite asked Zeus to judge which of them should receive the golden apple for being the most beautiful, but he refused to do so.

Why did Zeus decline? Would you be willing to judge such proud and powerful deities? What do you think would have happened to Zeus if he had judged the goddesses, one of whom was his wife? Explain.

The three goddesses who wanted the title of fairest each tried to bribe Paris, the judge, who was a son of the king of Troy. Hera offered him dominion over Europe and Asia. Athena promised him victory in all of his battles. Aphrodite offered him the most beautiful woman in the world.

Of these three choices, which would you take: dominion, victory, or love? Why? If you chose dominion or victory, what would you use it for? Write your thoughts below.

Helen was an astonishingly beautiful young woman. When Helen's father, Tyndareus, reviewed her suitors, he was afraid things might get out of hand. All of the powerful princes of Greece were presented as bachelors. To keep the rejected suitors from seizing Helen, he made all the princes promise to honor her decision and to attack anyone who did not.

Without fully knowing it, Tyndareus had created an alliance. What are the risks of belonging to an alliance like this? What are the advantages? Make a list of the advantages and disadvantages, and then name as many modern alliances as you can. Do you also belong to some sort of an alliance?

Before leaving Troy, Paris was warned by his brother and sister, the twins Helenus and Cassandra, not to pursue Helen. These twins were seers.

Paris ignored the pleas of the seers and of his countrymen. Why? Do you think Paris had a choice at this point? Explain your ideas.

Paris was led by Aphrodite to Sparta where Helen and her husband, Menelaus, entertained him. In the ancient world, travelers often relied on people they did not know for food and shelter. (In ancient Greek, the word *xenos* means both *stranger* and *guest*.) A similar practice still exists in Tibet, North Africa, and elsewhere.

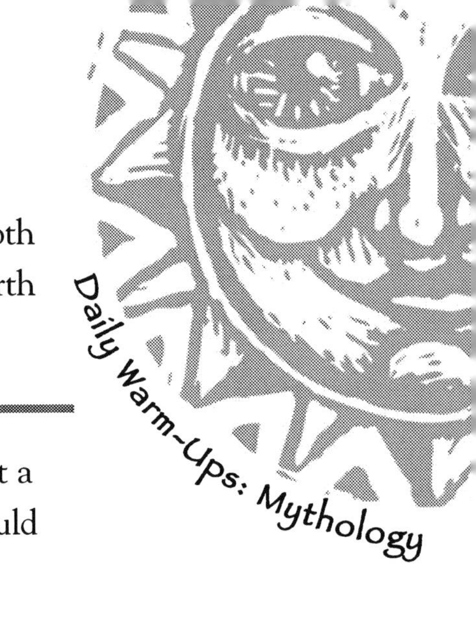

Describe how you would take a trip today. Would you sleep at a hotel or a relative's house? What means of transportation would you use? How does this differ from ancient travel?

Helen of Troy was so beautiful that her face was said to have "launched a thousand ships."

Explain what this saying means. Do you believe that the abduction of one person could spark a war?

Thetis understood that her son Achilles would die if he went to war. When the Greek allies began amassing a fleet to go to Troy, she dressed Achilles in a long robe and hid him among the young women in the court of Lycomedes. Odysseus, who was looking for Achilles, set down a collection of ornaments and weapons close to the women. When one of them fingered the weapons and paid no attention to the ornaments, Odysseus knew it was Achilles.

Write a paragraph about someone playing a similar trick on you. What would the scene look like? Name a specific object that you would be attracted to.

Strong winds from the north kept the Greek fleet from departing for Troy. Agamemnon was blamed for the bad weather because of a boast he had made against Artemis. Agamemnon agreed to sacrifice his daughter, Iphigenia, to appease the slighted Artemis. In one version of the story, Iphigenia became Artemis' priestess.

What does it mean to sacrifice something? Describe a difficult sacrifice you have made. What was difficult about it? Was the sacrifice worth what you gained by it?

Before the Greeks arrived in Asia Minor, an oracle told them that the first soldier to land would be the first one to die in battle. The soldier's name was Protesilaus, which means "first to jump ashore."

Protesilaus is described as being brave. Do you agree with this description? In a paragraph, explain what it means to be brave.

Menelaus and Odysseus became the representatives for the Greek army. They met with King Priam to discuss a solution to Paris' abduction of Helen and his theft of Spartan gold. Paris' many brothers were on his side. They defended his actions and called for war.

What would you have done to resolve this conflict between the Greeks and the Trojans? Who should have done what? The Trojan Antenor suggested returning Helen and the gold to the Greeks. Write a paragraph about a possible peaceful diplomatic solution to this conflict.

In preparing for an attack, the Greek army cut off Troy from the surrounding cities in Asia Minor. Troy was unable to trade with or get military aid from its neighbors.

The Trojan War lasted about a decade. What would happen if your city or town were cut off from the rest of the world for that long? How would it affect daily life? Write a paragraph about life under these conditions.

Ares, the god of war, fought for both the Trojans and the Greeks. His purpose was to encourage and prolong the battle. When the mortal Diomedes attacked Ares, the god's scream was as loud as that of ten thousand men.

Write a paragraph describing Ares. What kind of a character is he?

After nine years of conflict, a quarrel sprang up between two Greek warriors, Achilles and Agamemnon. Agamemnon had carried off the daughter of the priest of Apollo. In response, Apollo poured down fiery arrows from his sun-chariot. When Agamemnon was forced to return the girl, he took Achilles' attendant Briseis in her stead. Briseis had no say in the matter, which is often the case for women in classical mythology.

Write a paragraph about this incident from the point of view of Briseis. How do you think she felt?

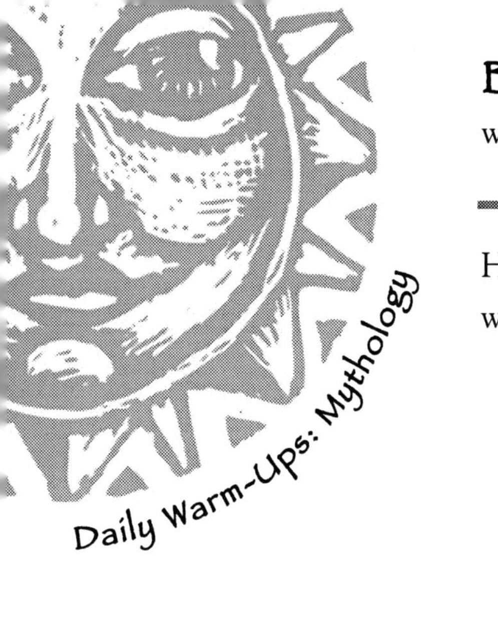

Both Achilles and Hector knew that they were doomed to die in the Trojan War.

How do you think this knowledge affected their fighting? How would such knowledge have affected you? Explain.

Menelaus and Paris had started the Trojan War. Helen was the wife of Menelaus. Paris had abducted Helen. Menelaus had followed Paris with an alliance of Helen's past suitors. After years of bloody fighting, the soldiers stopped, and Menelaus and Paris faced each other in single combat.

Imagine that you are a soldier, Trojan or Greek. Write a letter home describing your feelings about the fact that Menelaus and Paris are finally confronting each other.

The gods became heavily involved in the Trojan War. Thetis wanted the Greeks to lose. Hera wanted the Trojans to lose. Instead of helping the side they favored, the goddesses gave false counsel to the side they detested. Thetis suggested to Menelaus, through a dream, to fight when he should have stayed back. Hera persuaded Pandarus to shoot an arrow and break a truce when he should have remained peaceful.

Explain what the word *strategy* means. How would you describe the strategies of Thetis and Hera?

Athena appeared to Diomedes on the battlefield just before he rushed at Ares. She wanted to encourage him to have no fear. Ares was a terrifying and bloodstained god, but Diomedes gathered his courage and hurled his spear at the god of war.

Describe the most frightening thing that you have faced. How did you find the courage to confront it? What will be a difficult challenge for you in the future?

When Achilles was an infant, his mother dipped him in the River Styx, one of the rivers in the underworld. This made his body invulnerable to harm. The only place he could still be hurt was on his heel, where his mother held him as she dipped him in the water.

What is an "Achilles' heel"? Describe a contemporary person's Achilles' heel.

Achilles' parents were Peleus and Thetis. Thetis was a daughter of a sea god. When Peleus courted her, she changed her shape many times, becoming water, a lioness, and a cuttlefish. Peleus was told that Thetis would be his wife if he could hold on to her as she underwent all of these changes.

What does this story suggest about relationships? People change over time. What do couples have to do to endure this change? Explain your ideas.

In the opening line of the *Iliad*, the "rage" of Achilles is mentioned. After Agamemnon took Achilles' attendant, Achilles withdrew from the fighting. He was angry about being mistreated. The Greeks relied on his military skill and suffered in the battle without him.

Can you identify with Achilles? Describe what was happening in Achilles' mind as he waited in his tent, knowing that his allies were dying.

After asking his mother to make an offering to Athena, the Trojan Hector headed back to battle the Greeks. Seeing his family for the last time, he reached out for his young boy, who cringed at the hero's shining helmet and its tall plume.

This is an extraordinary moment: Hector is going into battle to defend his city, his personal honor, and his family honor. But as he leaves, his boy is too terrified to recognize his father. In a paragraph, describe how Hector and his little son felt.

Hera distracted Zeus, and the Greeks got the upper hand in fighting the Trojans. When Zeus caught on to Hera's plan, she denied that she was helping the Greeks and said it was Poseidon who was aiding them. This was true, but Poseidon was helping the Greeks because Hera had begged him to do so.

How would you describe Hera's behavior? If you were Poseidon, what would you say to Hera? Write the dialogue you and Hera would have.

Since Achilles would not fight with his fellow Greeks, his best friend, Patroclus, borrowed his armor and fought for him.

What effect would seeing the armor of the great Achilles have on the Trojans? Why? Explain.

Hector killed Achilles' friend Patroclus. Then Hector put on the armor that Patroclus had borrowed from Achilles.

What does it mean to wear another person's armor? What was signified by Hector's taking of the absent hero's helmet and breastplate? Write your ideas below.

Distraught over the death of his best friend, Achilles returned to battle. Because he had lost his armor to Hector, he wore a dazzling new suit of metal.

Do you feel different when you get something brand new? Have you ever had a new pair of running shoes and felt like you could run a little faster or farther? Describe how you think Achilles felt in his new armor.

Once Achilles decided to reenter battle and avenge the death of his best friend, Patroclus, he was uninterested in food and unwilling to feast before the fight. Odysseus said that the Greeks should eat before the battle.

Describe a time when you were so focused or determined that you forgot to do something basic like eating. How did such intense concentration feel? What were the consequences of such single-mindedness?

The Greeks were fighting in a foreign land, but the Trojans were fighting at home.

Who had a geographic advantage? Why? Explain your ideas.

Achilles finally faced Hector in battle.

At this late moment, was there anything Hector could have done to change the outcome of the war? Helen and the Spartan gold were still within the walls of Troy. Could Hector have returned them to the Greeks? If you were Hector, would you have faced Achilles? Write your thoughts below.

To get Hector to engage with Achilles, Athena disguised herself as Hector's brother and stood beside him. Athena was on the side of the Greeks, and she egged Hector on because she knew he would die if he fought Achilles.

What do you think of Athena's deception? Apollo, Hector's true ally, didn't even show up for Hector's last fight. What does this say about the gods? Describe their behavior and explain what you think of it.

After killing Hector, Achilles strapped the body behind his chariot and dragged the fallen warrior around Troy's walls. In the ancient world, this was considered an inhuman act.

Describe how Achilles must have felt to do such a thing.

Odysseus stole the Trojans' statue, called the Palladium, which was dedicated to Athena. Without this statue, some Trojans feared that Athena would cause more trouble for their city. When the Trojans found a wooden horse dedicated to Athena that the Greeks had left behind, supposedly as a gift, they brought it into their city.

What is meant by the phrase *Trojan horse*? Explain.

Cassandra knew that Greek warriors were hiding in the Trojan horse. In fact, Cassandra could predict many things. Her curse was that no one listened to her.

What would you do if you knew the future but no one listened to you? Cassandra always spoke her predictions. Could she have found another way to communicate her knowledge? Explain.

Sort the following names into one group of Trojans and one group of Greeks.

Menelaus	Paris
King Priam	Achilles
Agamemnon	Aeneas
Hector	Odysseus
Cassandra	Diomedes

Of all the heroes of the Trojan War, two had epics written about their post-war travels. One hero was Greek; Homer wrote about him. The other hero was Trojan, and the Roman poet Virgil wrote about him.

Who were these two veterans? What do you know about them? Think about some contemporary films or books about war veterans. What views of soldiers do these films or books show? How does this modern view compare with the classical view? Write a paragraph explaining your ideas.

Many Greek gods were adopted by the Romans and renamed.

Sort the following names of the gods and goddesses into two groups: one for Greek names, the other for Roman.

Demeter	Ceres
Vesta	Helios
Proserpine	Hestia
Dionysus	Sol
Bacchus	Persephone

Helen's cousin was Penelope, Odysseus' wife. When Helen reviewed the suitors of Greece, both Odysseus and Menelaus were there. Helen was famous for leaving Menelaus, but Penelope was famous for waiting for Odysseus to return from the Trojan War.

If your love had been gone for twenty years on a dangerous mission, would you wait for him or her? Would you ever leave a love, as Helen did? What does the word *fidelity* mean to you? Explain.

Many of the gods and heroes have more than one wife or girlfriend. Women are generally not allowed to have multiple husbands in classical mythology. Clytemnestra was chastised for taking a lover after her husband, Agamemnon, went to war. But Agamemnon thought he had a right to have Achilles' lover for himself.

What is a *double standard*? Is it fair that Clytemnestra was not allowed do something that Agamemnon could? Write a paragraph explaining your ideas.

Odysseus sailed from Troy to the southern tip of the Peloponnesus. He was almost home, but "almost" rarely counts. Nine days of bad weather blew him across the Mediterranean to North Africa, and then his real journey began.

Describe a time when you were very close to reaching or achieving something but didn't quite make it.

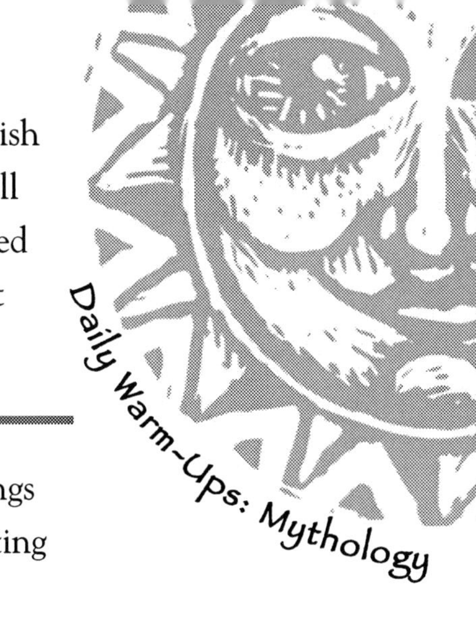

When three of Odysseus' men went ashore, they encountered the Lotus-eaters. These people fed on the yellowish fruit of the lotus. When the sailors tasted the fruit, they lost all their longing for home and forgot the pain of war. They wanted to stay in Lotus Land. Odysseus had to chain them to his boat to continue his journey.

What would it be like if you forgot all the difficult or bad things that had happened to you? What would be scary about forgetting your plans for the future? Explain your ideas in a paragraph.

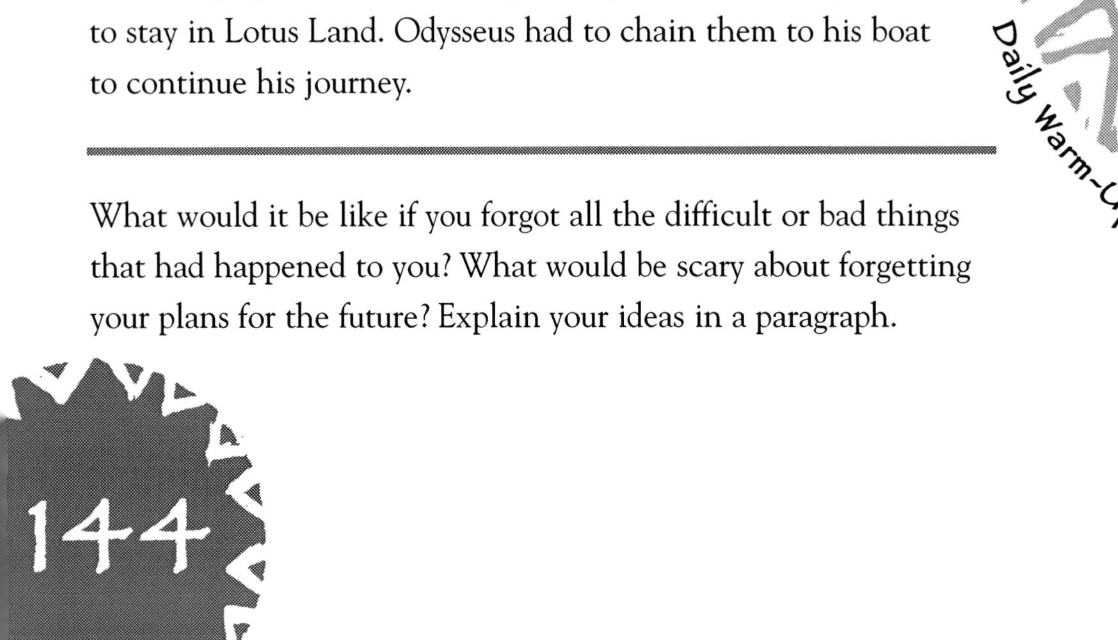

The Cyclops, a one-eyed giant, trapped Odysseus' crew and started to eat them. Odysseus blinded the Cyclops and rescued himself and his crew from the giant's cave by tying each man to the belly of a ram. They sneaked past the Cyclops as the giant let his rams out to graze.

Does this seem like a probable way to escape? Draw a picture of Odysseus' famous encounter with the Cyclops.

On the island of Aeolia, the king of that land gave Odysseus a curious gift in an ox-hide bag: He had tied up the contrary winds. Only the helpful west wind remained free, and it brought Odysseus' ship close to his home, Ithaca. But his crew could not keep from opening the gift, and the bad winds blew them back out to sea.

Does this story remind you of another myth? How are the stories similar? Describe a time when you could not keep from looking at or opening something.

Circe, a sorceress, changed half of Odysseus' crew into pigs and then fed them acorns. There was something greedy about the crew's intense desire for food and companionship.

If Circe changed you into an animal, what kind would it be? Why would a particular animal be appropriate for you? What would this animal show about human nature, or about you in particular? Write your ideas below.

Odysseus is often described as shrewd or a rogue.

What is a *rogue*? If you had fought in the Trojan War, would you have wanted Odysseus on your side? Why? Explain.

Penelope and Telemachus, Odysseus' son, wanted to wait for Odysseus to return, but their palace had been invaded by selfish suitors. These men treated Telemachus with contempt and demanded that Penelope choose a new husband. They ate and drank all the stores Penelope had in her palace.

How do you think the gods reacted to this behavior? Write a paragraph about this, remembering the importance of hospitality to the Greeks.

Penelope held a contest for the suitors. Odysseus was in the palace, disguised as a beggar so that he could assess the situation. The goal of the contest was to string Odysseus' old bow and shoot an arrow through the collar of a dozen ax heads. None of the suitors could even string the bow. The disguised Odysseus quickly rigged the bow and made a winning shot. His skill at using the bow was like a signature.

Describe something that only you can do among your family or friends. How does this talent make you feel?

To verify that the beggar was in fact Odysseus, Penelope played a trick on him. She asked her servants to move the marriage bed that Odysseus had built. The bed was supposed to be rooted in the ground. Odysseus became angry, thinking that someone had cut the roots of the bed. When Penelope saw this reaction, she knew the man was Odysseus.

Think about a person who is special to you. Then think about a secret or unique thing that only you and this person know. If you did not see this person for twenty years, what question could be asked to verify that you are both who you say you are? Write the person's name and the question you would ask.

The tale of Odysseus' long journey home is told in the epic poem the *Odyssey*.

Honda makes a minivan called the Odyssey. What is an *odyssey*? Why is this a particularly good name for a minivan and not a sports car or some other car model? Write your thoughts below.

The Roman goddess Victory was called Nike in Greek. This seems like a sound name for an athletic shoe. But modern knowledge of Greek and Roman mythology is often incomplete. Some companies have made big mistakes in naming their brands. In 1997, one company named a running shoe Incubus, only to find out that an incubus is an evil spirit that haunts women. The company had to pull tens of thousands of shoes off the shelves and rename them.

Using a proper noun from mythology, make up a bad or humorous name for a consumer product. Share your brand name with classmates.

Narcissus was a beautiful young man, but he arrogantly rejected every admiring girl. To punish him, Aphrodite caused him to see his own reflection in a pool on Mount Helicon. He was captivated by its beauty and fell in love with it. Narcissus stayed there, looking at himself, unable to touch the image. He was so caught up in his reflection that he forgot to eat and drink. He died of starvation.

What does it mean to be *narcissistic*? What did Narcissus do wrong? Why is being captivated by his own image appropriate for such a person? Explain.

Daedalus was a great inventor and architect. He built the Labyrinth for King Minos. According to Apollodorus, a group of Athenians escaped the maze, and King Minos blamed Daedalus. Imprisoned in his own invention, Daedalus and his son, Icarus, built two pairs of wings using feathers and wax. Instead of having to find their way through the maze, the wings would carry them up and away from the island of Crete. Daedalus told his son not to fly too close to the sun or too close to the water. Ignoring this advice, Icarus soared with joy high in the sky. The wax on his wings melted, and he plunged to his death in the sea.

What does this story say about Icarus? Describe how Icarus might have felt as he rose toward the sun.

Roman households had gods called Lares. A Lar was venerated as a personal family god. A Lar protected and defended the household. Sometimes a Lar was considered to be the spirit of an ancestor. Lares were not publicly worshipped.

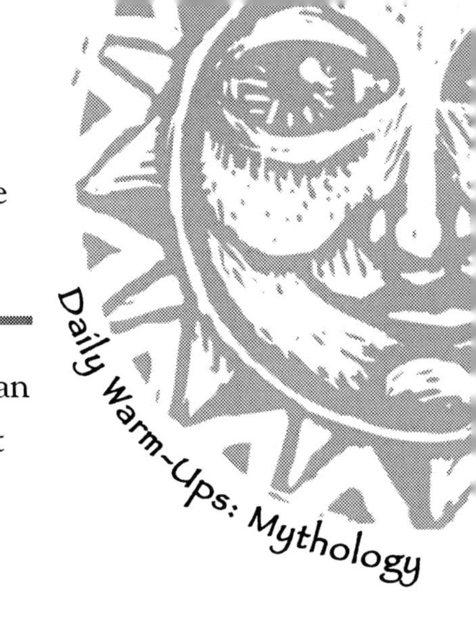

Do you have pictures of ancestors, a good luck figure, or even an old heirloom? Describe something in your house that could act as a modern Lar for your family. Write a paragraph about its ability to protect you.

Janus was the Roman god of doors. He had two faces, one looking forward and one looking back. He presided over bridges and passages. His chief temple ran east to west so that it could witness the beginning and the end of each day.

What month is named after Janus? Why is this an appropriate month for the god of doorways? Explain.

At the end of the Trojan War, Aeneas embarked on a journey similar to that of Odysseus. Troy had been completely destroyed. Aeneas took his father and son across the sea to look for a place to set down new roots.

Describe a perilous or an uncertain journey made by someone in your family. From what continent does your family originate? How far away would you be willing to move?

To avoid Scylla and Charybdis, Aeneas sailed around the western side of Sicily. There the ship met a castaway from the voyage of Odysseus who warned them of the dangerous Cyclopes. The castaway was starved and looked ragged in his threadbare clothes.

Castaways appear in the stories of Theseus, Odysseus, and Aeneas. What is a *castaway*? Describe what life would be like as a castaway.

Venus and Cupid worked together to encourage the queen of Carthage and Aeneas to fall in love with each other. The queen, Dido, was the founder of Carthage and was reluctant to give her love away. Greek and Roman mythology is filled with stories about people falling in love. Usually, the story states that Venus, Cupid, or both have directly caused the situation.

What do you think makes people fall in love? Have you ever felt affection for someone and not known exactly why? Describe that situation.

Dido asked Aeneas again and again to tell the story of his journey from Troy.

Long stories often change when we tell them multiple times. Do the facts of the stories that you tell remain the same? Do you sometimes elaborate? In a paragraph, relate how a story has been told to you in two different ways.

Aeneas grew comfortable in Carthage, and he delayed his departure for Italy. Mercury eventually found Aeneas in Carthage and asked him how much time he planned to waste in idle luxury. Aeneas was content, but he knew he had to fulfill his destiny.

Write a paragraph about a time when you gave up something easy and comfortable to move ahead and accomplish something difficult.

Looking for advice from his dead father, Aeneas visited the Elysian fields. This was a place for the blessed who had died but would eventually return to Earth. These transformed mortals played and sang in green meadows under a purple sun.

What would a paradise look like to you? Invent your own ideal place and describe it.

The Latins and Rutulians attacked the Trojans after they landed in Italy. Aeneas' son killed a beloved Latin stag unwittingly. Lavinia, a Latin princess, had been offered to Aeneas instead of to the King of the Rutulians. These events all angered the local people.

When foreign people establish themselves in a new place, friction sometimes follows. Imagine you are a Latin and write a paragraph about your fear of foreigners. In a second paragraph, imagine you are a Trojan and explain your need to establish a permanent home.

In search of a solution to the military opposition of the Latins and Rutulians, Aeneas visited Arcady. There he met a king named Evander. Evander could not help Aeneas with troops or money, but he gave him sound advice.

When we think of royalty, we imagine gold crowns and remarkable wealth. In classical mythology, kings are not always wealthy. What do the words *aristocracy* and *royalty* mean to you? Write a paragraph explaining your definitions.

The Trojan camp was surrounded by Rutulians. To get a message to Aeneas, two soldiers decided to leave the Trojan camp, pass through the enemy's camp, and find Aeneas. Young Euryalus was excited to try this dangerous mission. Nisus was older and more subdued.

Which figure do you identify with more? Do you like trying dangerous things? Would you never try something dangerous? Explain.

The Trojans and the Latins eventually married one another, and their descendants created the Julian house, from which Julius Caesar sprang. The Trojans won the right to rule the Latins, but these conquerors had to adopt the Latin language.

What did the Trojans lose in this agreement? What did the Latins lose? Would you rather have the right to govern a place, or to speak your own language? Explain.

Romulus was the mythical founder of Rome. He and his brother, Remus, were abandoned and partially raised by a she-wolf and a woodpecker.

Most cultures have myths that illustrate humans' dependence on the animal kingdom in a striking or an exaggerated way. List the ways in which you directly depend on animals.

Norse mythology comes from Scandinavia. In this tradition, the universe was created when a northern icy region called Niflheim began to interact with a southern fiery region called Muspell. The ice of the north began to melt and drip, and it formed a sleeping giant named Ymir.

Scandinavia comprises which countries? Does it make sense to you that ice would be involved in Norse mythology's creation myth? Why? Explain your ideas below.

Odin, Vili, and Ve, three important Norse gods, were walking on the shore of the great sea surrounding Midgard. They found two large pieces of wood and transformed them into the first man and woman, Ask and Embla. Odin gave them breath, Vili gave them thought and feeling, and Ve gave them hearing and sight.

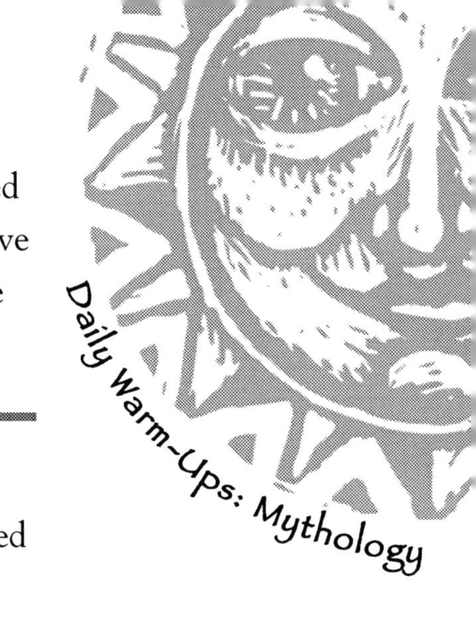

Forms are often repeated in the natural world. A twisted log can easily look like a human. List other forms you are reminded of by trees or flowers.

Odin gave one of his eyes to drink from the fountain of knowledge. He also offered himself in sacrifice: Odin hung on a giant tree, the Yggdrasil, for nine nights with a spear in his side. The Yggdrasil extends into the three realms of Norse mythology. After considerable suffering, Odin let out a scream and fell from the tree. Through his efforts, he had obtained the runes, a system of symbols for understanding and recording life.

What does it take to gain knowledge? Describe, in a paragraph, what you have done to learn something difficult.

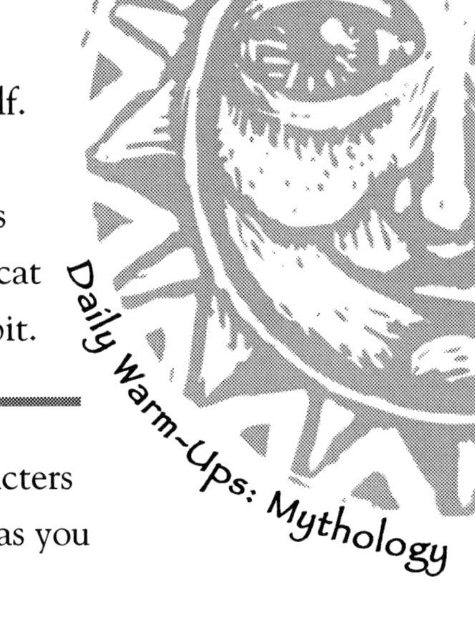

Odin needed to restrain the Fenris-wolf, who will devour Odin at the end of time. First he tried to chain the wolf. The metal links were immediately smashed. Odin then tried a restraint called Gleipnir. Unlike the metal chain, Gleipnir was made from the parts of many living organisms: the sound of a cat running, a woman's beard, bear sinews, fish breath, and bird spit.

What does the Gleipnir story say about biodiversity? Do characters in mythology have the same relationship to the environment as you do? How might their relationship be different? Explain.

Idun was the keeper of the Apples of Youth. This fruit gave the gods lasting youthfulness.

Why do you think an apple was chosen as a source and protection of youth? What connection might there be between apples and freshness or vigor? What would be odd about the Lima Beans of Youth or the Mushrooms of Youth? Write your thoughts below.

The hero Thor visited the gods at Utgard. He was unable to accomplish four simple tasks: waking up the giant Skrymir, drinking a horn of mead, lifting a cat off the ground, and wrestling an old woman. Thor thought he had failed, but he had been deceived. Thor actually smashed huge cracks in the earth when he tried to wake the giant. He drank the sea. He had lifted Midgard, the serpent of the universe. Finally, he fought impressively against old age.

Write a paragraph about Thor's situation. How do we know the things we experience are real? Should Thor have suspected something was wrong when he couldn't lift a cat off the ground?

Balder was a beloved son of Odin who suffered nightmares. Odin mounted his steed and rode to Niflheim to ask about his son's dreams. After Odin learned that Balder would be killed, Balder's mother, Frigg, traveled throughout the world and asked whatever she met never to hurt her son. Everything agreed. Disease, animals, fire, trees, and even stones swore they would not injure him. Then the gods gathered around Balder and pelted him with every manner of object. The boulders, swords, and clubs bounced off Balder, and the gods roared with laughter. They spent all night hurling things at Balder, but he was unharmed.

What do you think of this scene? Do you think it is funny or violent? Would you have thrown something at Balder? Write a paragraph about it.

Daedalus was clever. He built a pair of wings and found a way to thread a coiled seashell with a piece of string. Loki was also clever. While spending his days hiding from the gods in the form of a salmon and his nights sitting in a hideout, Loki invented a new type of net to catch fish.

What clever modern inventions do you use? List them. Can you name some of the people who invented them?

The world of humans, Midgard, is connected to the world of the gods, Asgard, by a rainbow bridge. The bridge allows gods to travel back and forth, but humans and giants are unable to climb it.

Rainbows have various meanings in most of the world's religions and mythologies. With what do you associate rainbows? Do they have any special meaning for you? Are they just an optical effect? Explain.

Odin, Thor, and Frigg all have parts of our calendar named after them.

Write what parts these are below. (Remember that Odin is sometimes called Woden.)

Unlike Olympus, Asgard, home of the Norse gods, is often a somber place. Bravery was exalted as the greatest human characteristic, but there is a sense in Norse mythology that the ultimate fate of people and the gods is collapse. Evil will eventually destroy Asgard.

Mythology concerns the fate of humankind at many levels. Write a paragraph detailing your feelings about the idea of fate.

The emblem of Thor is his hammer, Miollnir. Zeus is associated with his thunderbolt. Objects often have connotations. They put us in a certain mood or make us think about certain concepts. A flower might make one think about beauty or spring. Gods have objects with which they are associated. These objects say something about their characters.

With what objects are you associated? Make a list of three objects and explain why each one would make a good emblem for you.

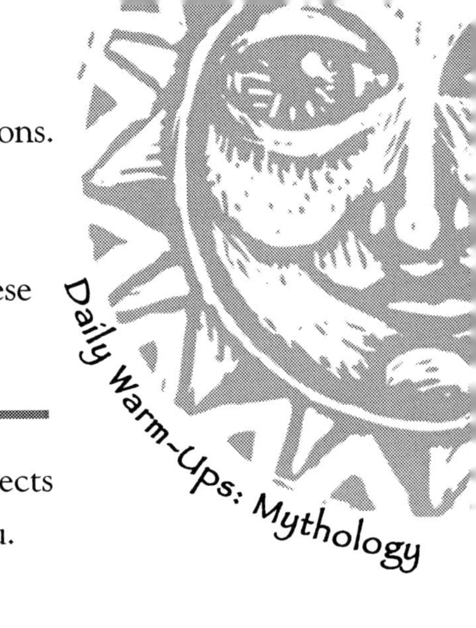

1–3. Answers will vary.
4. Nyctophobes fear night. Other answers will vary.
5. 1. d, 2. c, 3. b, 4. a
6. Answers will vary.
7. A Pandora's box is anything that once opened will cause unmanageable problems.
8. Answers will vary.
9. The dramatists are Aeschylus, Euripides, and Sophocles. *Classical* means a period or a form of art considered to represent the height of achievement.
10. Answers will vary.
11. d
12. c
13. Like a conventional birth, Athena's was painful, and Zeus needed help to deliver. Unlike a conventional birth, the one giving birth was male, and the offspring was an adult. Other answers will vary.
14–17. Answers will vary.
18. Answers will vary. Students may conclude that the story ends unhappily. This is the usual outcome when mortals try to do what only gods can do.
19. Answers will vary.
20. c; Dawn and moonlight are closely related to the sun. (Both are actually created by the sun.)
21–22. Answers will vary.
23. c; Other answers will vary.
24. Answers will vary.
25. Answers will vary. Students may suggest that wealth has its costs, and that wishes can be dangerous.
26–27. Answers will vary.
28. Drawings will vary.
29–30. Answers will vary.
31. Atlas turned to stone. He became the Atlas Mountains in Morocco and Algeria.
32. The Greek gods are Zeus, Poseidon, Athena, Aphrodite, and Ares. The Roman gods are Jupiter, Neptune, Minerva, Venus, and Mars.

33–35. Answers will vary.
36. The story illustrates the changing of the seasons. Modern people know that the seasons are caused when the earth receives more or less direct sunlight.
37–38. Answers will vary.
39. Sentences will vary. This punishment is perfect for Tantalus because he was always hungry to impress people, particularly with food.
40–41. Answers will vary.
42. The Greek gods are Hera, Artemis, Hermes, and Hephaestus. The Roman gods are Juno, Diana, Mercury, and Vulcan.
43–45. Answers will vary.
46. Drawings will vary.
47. Oedipus said the creature was "man." Other answers will vary.
48–49. Answers will vary.
50. Something is ironic when there is a discrepancy between the expected and the actual state of affairs.
51. Answers may vary somewhat. In general, because Oedipus was not able to see something so important, right under his nose, he blinded himself. Also, he was ashamed and could not bear to look at his family or friends.
52. Answers will vary.
53. 1. b, 2. a, 3. e, 4. f, 5. d, 6. c
54. 1. c, 2. b, 3. a, 4. d, 5. f, 6. e
55. Answers will vary.
56. The king was afraid of Heracles' brute strength. Answers may vary somewhat.
57–69. Answers will vary.
70. Drawings will vary.
71. Answers will vary.
72. 1. e, 2. d, 3. b, 4. c, 5. a, 6. f
73. 1. f, 2. e, 3. a, 4. b, 5. d, 6. c
74–87. Answers will vary.
88. Heracles' labors included the Nemean lion, the Lernaean Hydra, the Stymphalian birds, the Golden Apples, and Cerberus. The Argonauts' adventures included the Lemnian

wives, the Dolione tribe, the Harpies, the Clashing Rocks, and Scylla and Charybdis.

89–96. Answers will vary.

97. Theseus attached one end of the twine to the opening of the maze and carried the rest of the twine with him. After Theseus killed the Minotaur, he followed the twine back to where he entered. Other answers will vary.

98–99. Answers will vary.

100. Three critical features of a democracy are the rights to assemble, debate, and vote. Theseus is said to have brought these rights to Athens. Other answers will vary.

101–104. Answers will vary.

105. Drawings will vary.

106–122. Answers will vary.

123. An Achilles' heel is a flaw that causes someone to fall, a place where a strong person is vulnerable. Other answers will vary.

124–135. Answers will vary.

136. A Trojan horse is a person or device deliberately set to bring about an enemy's downfall or to undermine from within.

137. Answers will vary.

138. The Greek side included Achilles, Odysseus, Agamemnon, Menelaus, and Diomedes. The Trojan side included Paris, King Priam, Hector, Aeneas, and Cassandra.

139. The Greek veteran was Odysseus, and the Trojan veteran was Aeneas.

140. The Greek gods are Demeter, Hestia, Helios, Persephone, and Dionysus. The Roman gods are Ceres, Vesta, Sol, Proserpine, and Bacchus.

141. Answers will vary.

142. A double standard is a practice allowing greater freedom or opportunity to one rather than another. Other answers will vary.

143–147. Answers will vary.

148. A rogue is a dishonest or an unprincipled person; a rascal. Other answers will vary.

149–151. Answers will vary.

152. An odyssey is a long series of wanderings or an adventurous journey. Without being too cumbersome, a minivan has enough storage space for such a trip.
153. Answers will vary.
154. To be narcissistic is to have excessive self-love. Other answers will vary.
155–156. Answers will vary.
157. The month of January is named for Janus. This is an apt namesake for the god of doorways because one year ends and another begins.
158. Answers will vary.
159. A castaway is an abandoned or a shipwrecked person. Other answers will vary.
160–168. Answers will vary.
169. Scandinavia includes Denmark, Norway, Sweden, Finland, and Iceland. Other answers will vary.
170–177. Answers will vary.
178. Days of the week are named after Odin, Thor, and Frigg. Wednesday is named after Odin. Thursday is named after Thor. Friday is named after Frigg.
179–180. Answers will vary.